FARM

SHAPES

EVERY DRAWING BEGINS WITH A FEW SIMPLE SHAPES.
IF YOU CAN MASTER THESE, YOU CAN DRAW ANYTHING!

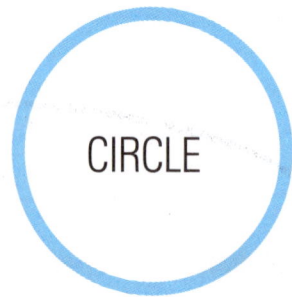

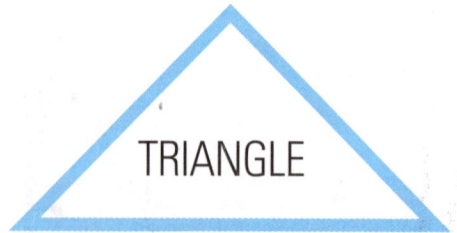

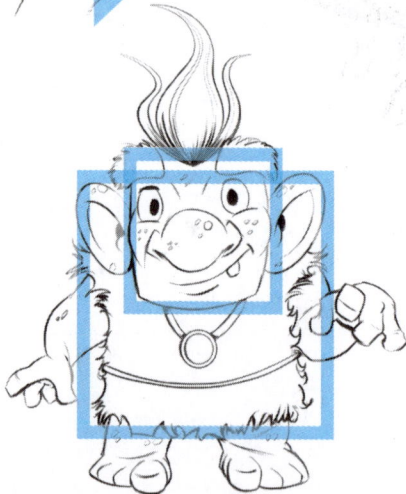

CIRCLE

TRIANGLE

SQUARE

Tools and Techniques

TO CREATE AN AWESOME DRAWING,
YOU'LL ONLY NEED A FEW THINGS:

PENCILS

CRAYONS

COLORED PENCILS

PAPER

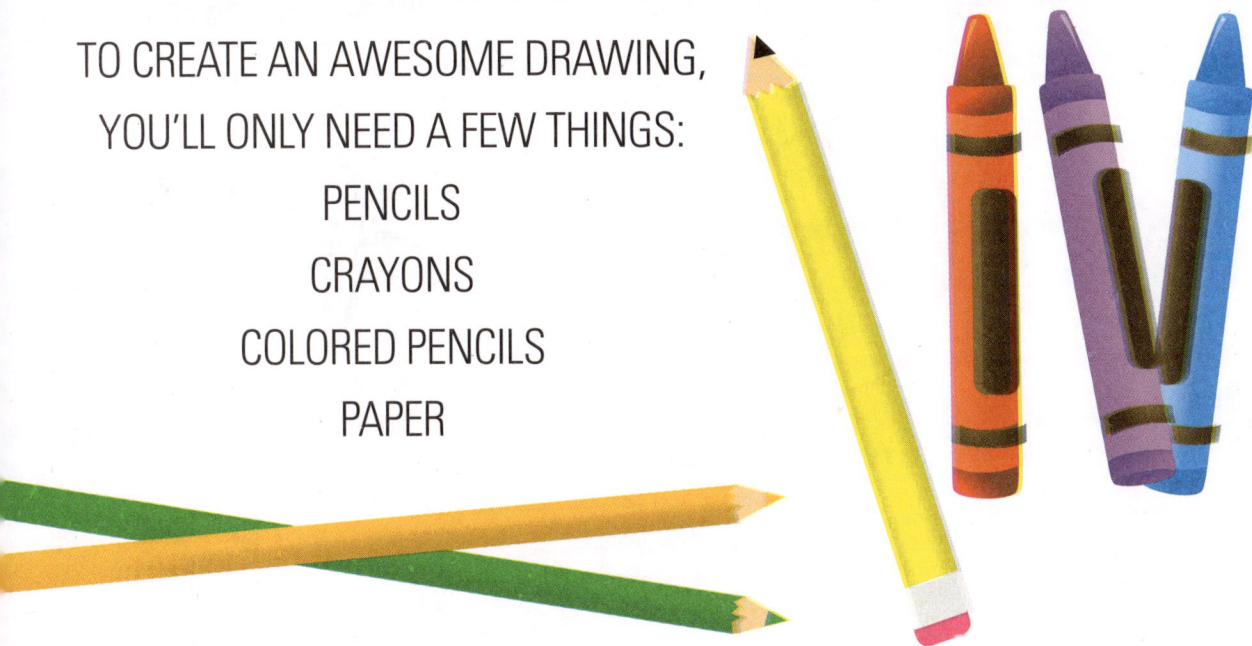

PRACTICE USING YOUR TOOLS HERE

FARM

1.

2.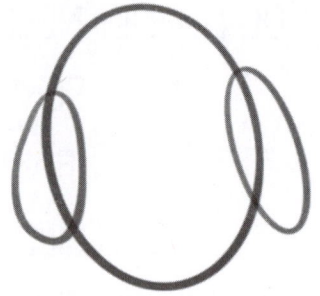

3.

4.

5.

Baby Chick

READY? NOW YOU TRY!

FARM

1.

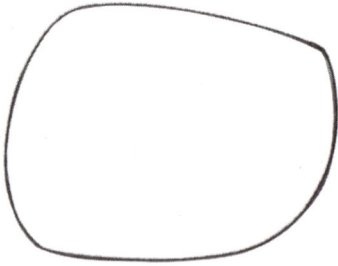

2.

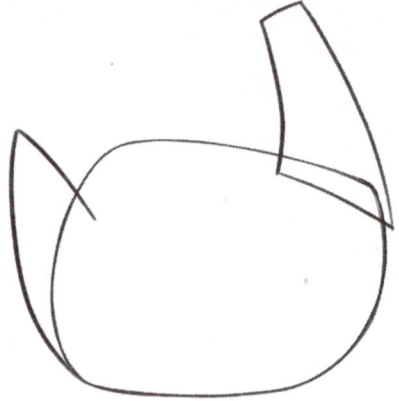

3.

4.

5.

Chicken

READY? NOW YOU TRY!

FARM

1.

2.

3.

4.

5.

Pig

READY? NOW YOU TRY!

FARM

1.

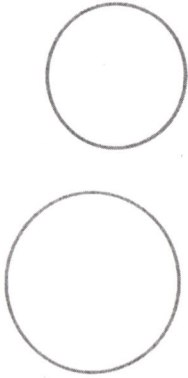

2.

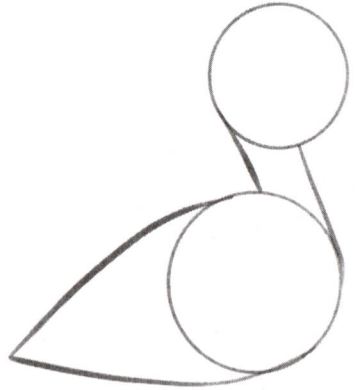

3.

4.

5.

Duck

READY? NOW YOU TRY!

FARM

1.

2.

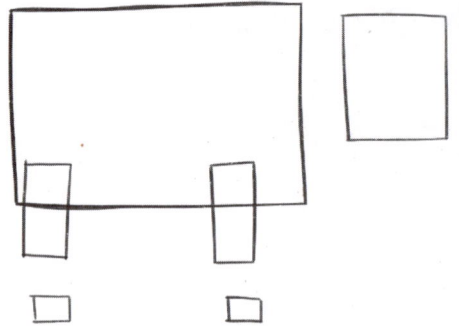

3.

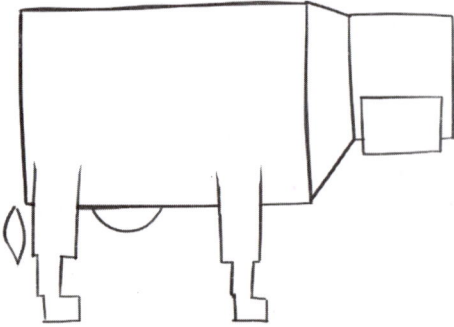

4.

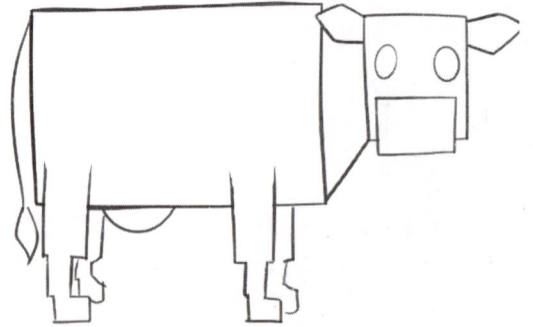

5.

READY? NOW YOU TRY!

1.

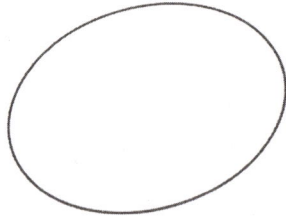

2.

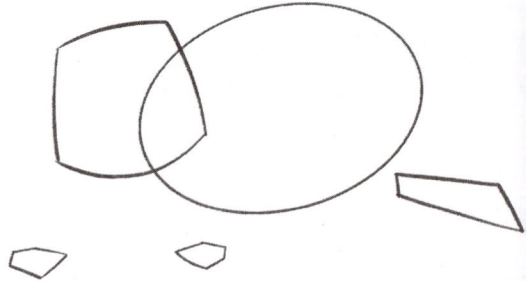

3.

4.

5.

Mouse

READY? NOW YOU TRY!

FARM

1.

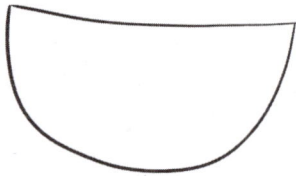

2.

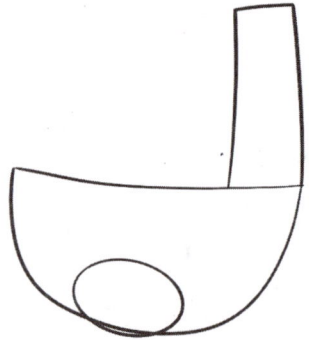

3.

4.

5.

Rooster

READY? NOW YOU TRY!

FARM

1.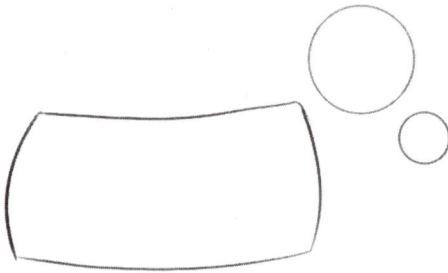

2.

3.

4.

5.

HORSE

READY? NOW YOU TRY!

FARM

1.

2.

3.

4.

5.

Goat

READY? NOW YOU TRY!

FARM

1.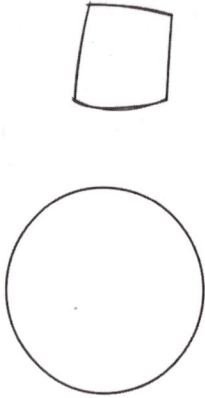

2.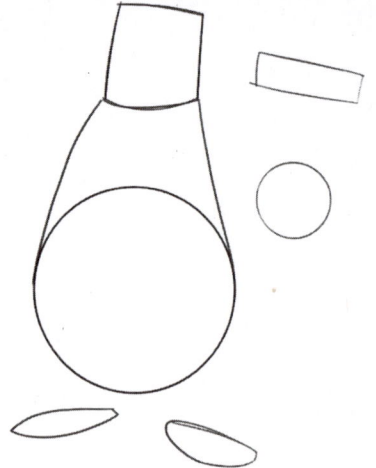

3.

4.

5.

FARMER

READY? NOW YOU TRY!

FARM

GREAT JOB! YOU'VE LEARNED TO DRAW ALL OF THE FARM ANIMALS. KEEP PRACTICING, AND HAVE FUN!